Calm Your Mind

SLEEP IN ABSOLUTE PEACE

Make The Choice To Have A Restful Night

ROSS GRIFFIN

Table of Contents

Chapter 1:

Improving Your Sleeping Habits

Sleeping habits are an important part of growth. It is sad how most people have degraded sleep and it has turned out to be a measure of laziness. If you truly want to know the importance of sleep, deprive yourself of it for a few days and watch how your body will respond. The importance of sleep cannot be over-emphasized. Have you noticed how fresh and strong you feel after waking up from a long and satisfying sleep? It is not the short naps and siestas during the day but the total rest that you get at night. You should constantly improve your sleeping habits. There are bad sleeping habits as well as good ones.

Here is a whole list about them and how they can be remedied:

1. Sleeping Late

Pushing daytime tasks into the night will not make you perform any better. Sometimes you may find yourself sleeping late because you did not realize time flies as you were storytelling. This is not enough justification. The remedy to sleeping late is developing a sleep schedule with consistent times to go to bed and wake up. Healthy sleep should be at least 8 hours long and uninterrupted. Depending on what time you want to wake up, observe bedtime time.

2. Sleeping With Tight Clothes

Some people sleep in tight clothes at night. This is unhealthy because sleep is a time of rest, and your body should feel free. Comfort during sleep is important. The remedy to sleeping in tight clothes is having nightclothes – a night dress or pajamas. They are highly recommended because they are tailored to factor in comfort during sleep. Do not sleep in jeans or clothes that you had during the day.

3. Constantly Checking Your Phone When You Go to Bed

Most 'modern' people are guilty of this crime – addiction to mobile phones. They carry their phones when going to bed (which is okay) but misuse them in bed. The misuse is that they start checking their social media and browser feeds when it is bedtime. The remedy to this misuse of mobile phones and other electronics is putting them aside when going to bed. This is not enough. Switch your phone to silent mode or turn on do not disturb (DND). Continued phone notifications will interrupt your sleep.

4. Listening To Music As You Sleep

The habit of listening to music on your earphones or speaker when you have gone to bed is unhealthy. Music may soothe you into sleep at the beginning, but it is a distraction that many people love. No matter how loveable it is, loud music will deprive you of sleep. The remedy to listening to music in bed is that you do not use your earphones and lower the volume when playing on the speaker. Soft music will make you fall asleep. You can also set the music to switch off after about one hour or so because you would have fallen asleep already.

5. Oversleeping

Sleeping is good but too much of it is unhealthy. Sleep must be regulated. You should neither go to bed late nor wake up late. Find a balance between the two and you shall optimize the importance of sleep. The remedy to oversleeping is setting an alarm. It will help you wake up early and as well as observe your sleeping schedule. Alarms are noisy and you should check-up with your roommate if they are comfortable with it (especially if it goes off early in the morning).

Conclusion

Sleep is important for your well-being. Great sleeping habits will make you sleep better and healthier. Observe the remedies to these five bad sleeping habits to be on the safe side.

Chapter 2:

Stop Worrying and Go to Sleep

What are we meant to do when we have had a long day and we are finally on our bed but cannot sleep? We cannot let go of all the headaches we go through every day all day long. How can we reset the memories or only the guilt and remorse that we keep carrying each day?

We all want to give up everything for just a good night's sleep, but rarely do we get to enjoy one. We all want everything to be simple and easy for just a short while but, the reality is, we are ready to let go!

I know that life is not a fairy tale, and we all have harsh realities that need to be dealt with. But why is that we can't let it get easy even when nothing is wrong in our life?

We are so used to taking pressure that sometimes we feel normal to be so sucked into these unnecessary and unhealthy things. Don't get me wrong, but the pressure is important. Pressure makes you feel like a human and makes us feel like we are the superior of all beings. But staying under the pressure by choice is something that you should never get accustomed to.

Why is it that you are always in need of searching for something that keeps you away from happiness? You have made this false scenario in your head that if everything is wrong and if you close your eyes for just one small moment, everything might turn upside down.

This behavior has spun this emotional roller coaster in us, that does not let us give up on anything even when we are at our lowest.

You have to understand a simple concept. You are an integral part of everyone's life around you. But you are no good to them if you cannot live a long, happy and healthy life. A life in which you have not dedicated enough time to them, by sharing their feelings and your pain with them.

You need some time off not only for your well-being but indirectly, for them to have you in their lives.

You have to get rid of your past. Get rid of your pains for just a portion of your day or night in that case. Just so you don't seem like a life-less moving object, who talks only when you ask them something.

Be open, be transparent, be indulging, be engaging and be interesting so that you are worth caring for. You cannot expect sympathy and emotions if you are not willing or are not capable of giving something in return.

For that, you need to give your brain some time to shut down and reset. Your brain has an optimal limit to work on its peak, So does your body.

Your body and your brain work in sync to make you look like a proper human being. So don't get in your way to happiness and satisfaction.

So, drop all your anxieties and worries and go to sleep. If you have regrets about doing it, think of it as you are paying back to your body and your loved ones. Paying back for everything that they do to keep you safe and active.

Chapter 3:

How To Fall Asleep Faster

Insomnia is the most common sleep disorder, with up to <u>30%</u> of adults reporting short-term sleep issues. But if you've been up at night wondering how to fall asleep fast, it might be affecting you even more than you realize.

<u>Failing to fall asleep</u> isn't only frustrating — the anxiety from not being able to sleep can actually make it even harder to fall asleep in the future. So how can you stop this domino effect to successfully catch some zzz's?

1. Try the Military Method

The military method is a technique that focuses on muscle relaxation, breathing, and mental visualization. Here's how to fall asleep fast with the military method.

- Sit or lay down on your bed, slowly relaxing the muscles in your body.
- Beginning with your face, tense your muscles then allow them to loosen naturally. Begin to take deep, calming breaths.
- Repeat this process until your entire body feels completely at ease.
- Push all thoughts from your head for 10 seconds. When your brain feels clear, picture one of the following scenarios:

- Peacefully lying in a canoe on a calm lake
- Gently rocking back and forth in a completely dark room

If the above is unsuccessful, mentally repeat "don't think, don't think, don't think" for at least 10 seconds, and try again.

2. Use The 4-7-8 Method

The 4-7-8 method is based on Pranayama, a traditional yoga technique. This method can help ease anxiety and lull you into a state of calm. In the 4-7-8 technique, you focus on counting to distract yourself from feelings of anxiety. Here's how to sleep faster with the 4-7-8 method.

- While laying down in bed, allow your tongue to relax behind your front teeth, resting on the roof of your mouth.
- Slowly exhale all of your breath through your mouth, completely emptying your lungs.
- Breath in through your nose for 4 seconds, hold your breath for 7 seconds, then exhale for 8 seconds.

Repeat this process at least four times.

3. Try to Stay Awake

An unexpected strategy for trying to fall asleep fast is actually to try to stay awake. While it may sound counterintuitive, trying to stay awake can help you <u>lessen the anxiety</u> around trying to fall asleep.

Since falling asleep is an involuntary process, taking your mind off of the task at hand can give your brain the break it needs for you to stop counting sheep.

4. Turn Down Your Tech

With the prevalence of modern technology, surfing the internet before bed is more of a given than a question. While it can be tough to turn off your tech, looking at your screen before bed can <u>negatively impact your quality of sleep</u>. Many devices emit a blue light that simulates sunlight — and while this is helpful before your morning coffee, it can do more harm than good when trying to hit the hay.

If you're not able to completely part with your devices for an hour before bed, consider turning down your tech instead. Try listening to music, a calming podcast, or an audiobook for screen-free entertainment while you get ready for bed.

5. Don't Worry If You Don't Fall Asleep Instantly

Is it possible to fall asleep in five minutes? Many people make the mistake of trying to fall asleep almost instantly but going from wide awake to snoozing isn't always like flipping off a switch.

Instead, start to wind down around an hour before bedtime, slowly setting up a sleep-friendly environment in your bedroom by dimming your lights and relaxing your body.

6. Try Autogenic Training

Autogenic training is a relaxation method created by Johannes Heinrich Schultz, a German psychiatrist. Based on the principles of hypnosis, autogenic training uses a series of statements to create a calming effect in your nervous system. Here's how to fall asleep fast with autogenic training methods.

- Lay down and bring focus to your breath, saying to yourself, "I am completely calm."
- Bring your focus to your arms and repeat to yourself, "My arms are very heavy," then, "I am completely calm," at least six times.
- Move your focus to your legs and repeat to yourself, "My legs are very heavy," then, "I am completely calm," at least six times.
- Move around to different parts of your body, such as your abdomen, forehead, and heart, repeating the above phrases at least six times.
- Once you feel relaxed, begin to shift your attention to your entire body, where you should then feel relaxed and warm.
- Repeat the above steps until you're ready, at which point you can open your eyes (if you haven't yet fallen asleep) and enjoy the state of calm.

Chapter 4:

How To Stop Worrying and Go To Sleep

Have trouble falling asleep, staying asleep or just feeling rested? The bad news is that it may be due to personal lifestyle habits. However, the good news is that those are easy to change to help get you on your way to sleeping better. Some people lay in bed staring at the ceiling in part due to chronic pain, depression, medications, or other substances that can interfere with sleep. When you treat those issues, often it will naturally help improve your ability to sleep.

However, despite addressing other medical or psychiatric conditions, sleep difficulties often will persist. People who have chronic insomnia worry excessively about sleep and the effects of insomnia. They also become more and more agitated and tense as bedtime gets closer. If you're very worried about getting good sleep, you can put a lot of effort into getting sleep and have a lot of anxiety at night. This makes you more alert and can keep you lying in bed wide awake.

We are offering some suggestions that can help improve your sleep habits, including individuals who suffer from chronic insomnia. Trying to break some of the patterns that you may have developed is often the key.

Keep Your Sleep Schedule The Same

You can improve your sleep by ensuring that you have a consistent sleep schedule. Avoid staying up late on weekends and sleeping in, then trying to go to bed at your regular time on Sunday night. We call it social jet lag because it's like you've flown to California, and now you're trying to adjust back to the time zone difference. So, keep those times as consistent as you can." Going to bed early or sleeping in to catch up only leads to more fragmented and poor quality sleep. Typically, you go to bed two hours early and then just lay there wide awake, continuing to associate your bed with not sleeping.

Take Some Quiet Time Before Bedtime

Quiet time is worth its weight in gold. Give yourself at least 30 to 60 minutes of quiet, relaxed time before bed as a buffer. Nix phone screen time and replace it with reading a book, listening to calming music, taking a warm bath or having some decaffeinated herbal tea.

Distract Yourself If You Can't Sleep

If you can't fall asleep, get up and try to restart by doing something to distract yourself before going back to bed. It could be flipping through magazines, calming yoga stretches or some type of relaxing hobby like knitting or colouring. Avoid anything that's goal-directed or too physically or mentally activating such as house chores, paying bills or working on a computer. While it may be tempting to grab your phone off your nightstand and scroll endlessly through social media, don't. The blue light emitted from your phone or tablet screen can inhibit your natural melatonin production which is a hormone that is involved in the timing of our internal circadian sleep clock.

Learn How To Relax

Learning relaxation techniques such as meditation, guided imagery and progressive muscle relaxation can go a long way in helping you fall asleep. A sleep specialist can help you learn this as well as ways to calm your mind and your muscles and reduce or eliminate all the racing thoughts and worries. Dealing with stress in a healthy way is important for not only sleep, but your overall health, too. "Practice the relaxation techniques and develop them as a skill during the day when you feel good and are already calm, rather than trying to do them for the first time at bedtime,"

Keep A Sleep Log

Think of this as the adult sister to that diary you've kept in middle school. You can track the details of your sleep patterns and lifestyle habits. This can help you see trends in your behaviour and will be useful when you discuss your insomnia with your doctor or a sleep disorder specialist. If writing things down the old-fashioned way isn't your jam, try smartphone apps or your smartwatch to help you keep a log.

Chapter 5:

How To Develop Healthy Sleep Patterns For Success

Sleep And Success

There is a solid relationship between sleep and success. It sounds ironic that the traditionally perceived enemy of success could have any contribution to success. The truth is that the two are joined to the hip. There is no success without sleep.

You must have tried at one point to stay awake and continue with whatever you are doing. It could be because you had insufficient time and extending into the night was the only alternative you were left with. What happened? Your body involuntarily shuts down. Your eyes could no longer stay open, and your mind could think no more. Every part of your body was demanding (not asking) for rest.

The human anatomy has it that sleep is an important part of the human cycle. You can only postpone it up to a point where your body can no longer be awake. This is just a preview of the importance of sleep.

Above its importance, some people have poor sleeping patterns. It is not enough to sleep. Healthy sleep patterns are important for your success.

Here are some of them:

1. Regular Sleeping and Waking Up Times

Our bodies are like machines. They require service (food) as well as they require rest (sleep). You adapt to your sleeping patterns over some time. This makes it important to have regular times for the same because you will wake up the following day feeling healthy and re-energized.

Irregular sleeping patterns should be highly discouraged if you are pursuing success. As much as you have to work hard in your work or business, you equally need to pay attention to the time you have set for rest.

Do not extend working late into the night often because it will interrupt your sleeping habits. You will still be sleepy the following day.

2. Do Not Abuse Drugs

Drug abuse is one of the major causes of insomnia. Drugs can deprive you of sleep. You will stay awake even if you go to bed early.

While some people think it is okay to force yourself to be awake by using drugs, it is only a matter of time before they realize they were wrong. Khat, for example, will completely mess up with your sleep and leave you intoxicated.

Apart from denying you sleep; it will impair your judgment. This is the last thing you want for yourself if you want to be successful.

3. Do Not Be A Workaholic

No matter how much work holism is justified these days, the fact will remain that it is a damaging act that any sane person can indulge in.

This is an unhealthy practice that will disrupt your sleeping schedule. Have enough time to sleep as well as work. Put boundaries between them that will make you respect each other.

4. Prioritize Your Health

The easiest way to have healthy sleep patterns is to put your health first before anything else. This is very reasonable. You cannot work if you are sick, neither can you do all the things you want.

From a professional point of view, doctors will advise you to sleep at least eight hours a day. It could be quite a high threshold given that you may have a lot of work with little time.

When you prioritize your health, you will live to see another day.

5. Sleep Comfortably

Sleeping is an act of rest. For healthy sleep, ensure you sleep on a soft surface that will be comfortable for your body. You should not sleep while sitting. Sleep horizontally on a flat surface for your body to be at total rest.

It is equally very recommended to sleep in a calm environment. Nothing will interrupt your sleep until you wake up after having enough rest.

You have to make a lot of sacrifices to develop healthy sleep patterns for success.

Chapter 6:

Create Your Own Calm

What is it in your life that you feel most disconnected from? What is it that makes you want to creep back into your room? What things do you think have the most drastic effect on your personality and your behavior?

We all have some incidents in our past where we were so uncomfortable that it wasn't even funny from someone else's perspective. I mean, if I were to look at someone being miserable around something or someone for even a little moment, I might enjoy their misery. But why should you be like that?

Things that happen in and around us, have a purpose. You shouldn't get anxious and depressed about every little odd thing that happens to you!

Coping is a quality and an ability that can make people fly high without even knowing their source.

Look at it for an instance, you are a hard-working employee. You have been working for the past decade. You have given countless hours to your job and this company. You have always shown up on time and have always been the last one to leave the office. Yet you are not the brightest crayon in the box.

You might not be getting your effort's worth. But you have been doing this job for the longest time in your life. And you are content with what you have right now. Even if not, at least you are not hasty for something that doesn't suit you.

You might be an A-grade student, and you might be a chess club president. But you are not the cool guy or girl that everyone aspires to be. But you are ok with that because you are content with the attention that you have right now.

You might be content with your culture, your wealth, your friends, your partner because you are in a space where you feel the safest. You are not getting out of your way to achieve these extra things because you realize that what you have right now is good and I am happy with everything.

But let's say if you are not happy with what you have, what can you do to make an environment where things create a sense of calm and relaxation for you? How can you create a space where you feel nourished and nurtured?

Look for anything around you that makes you feel like you have a relation and a history with. Any item that brings you some nostalgia and a sense of relaxation that you once had with it in your past.

Collect all these things, may those be furniture, books, clothes, people, pets, even smells. You need to understand that you have all the good things lying around you. You just need to look out for them. You cannot go around saying you are unhappy just because on bad thing happened at a certain time at a certain place.

Life is a circus where some acts make you close your eyes out of fear, but most make you feel more alive and more excited for the next one. So, enjoy it like one!

Chapter 7:

Five Ways To Get Calm

The Art of Maintaining Calm

Calmness is an art that only a few people have mastered. Most people are erratic and easily unsettled by trivial matters. The state of calmness provides an optimum environment to work and meet your targets.

The modern world is full of people who seek solace in different deviations. They hope to find peace in a chaotic world. However, they only find temporary solutions to their problems and fail to secure calmness of mind and spirit.

Here are five ways to get calm:

1. **Regulate Your Body's Metabolism**.

We may find ourselves in circumstances that make our bodies tense. We experience an adrenaline rush as a natural body response to tension. Our hearts beat faster, a pang of fear laced with anxiety sweeps through our minds, and we are unable to make sober decisions.

Calmness becomes elusive and we often act out of fear of the unknown.

In such circumstances, our actions are not backed up by any rational thinking. How can we regain our composure and maintain calm? First, inhale sharply and exhale slowly to release the tension building up.

Repeat it until you manage to regulate your breathing. Inhaling and exhaling at regular intervals will bring calmness to replace the initial tension. Try to act as normal as possible and do not yield to any pressure to act, real or perceived.

2. Master Your Emotions

It takes great courage to master your emotions and reactions towards issues. A great man is capable of controlling his emotions and bringing calmness in chaotic situations. Calmness hardly prevails when emotions are high.

Emotions rid you of rationality and independent thinking. They control your actions and seek justification. Emotions are no respecter of persons. They have caused the downfall of many giants who did not let reason prevail.

Take charge of your emotions and do not yield to their temptations no matter how justifiable they may look. A master of emotions will bring calmness in their lives, and they can settle things soberly.

3.   Question Your Feelings

Your feelings are not always right. You could be biased and inclined to support certain things that disrupt calmness and are fodder to chaos. Subconscious feelings often present themselves as the truth and we believe unfounded theories that pose a danger to interpersonal relationships and by extension, societal harmony.

Calmness prevails where feelings and intuitions are evaluated before being acted upon. Learn to question your feelings and leave nothing to chance. For example, why do you hate the guard at the main gate or a political competitor? It is unfair to yourself not to understand the reason for the strong positions you take.

After questioning your feelings, you can re-evaluate hardline stances that you took which can jeopardize your calmness around people you consider hostile. You can manage to be calm and tolerant when you find no merit in your ill feelings towards something.

4.   Question What You Stand to Benefit or Lose

The chief question you should be able to answer is what you benefit from any chaos. There is disorderliness in the absence of calm, and it causes more harm than good. We are exposed to the risk of loss when the environment we live in is unstable. It is important to ensure it is calm for us to thrive in it and achieve our goals.

Many things run in the mind when one is provoked. What often skips the brain is whether or not the whole experience will be gainful. At this juncture, you think in retrospect concerning your life. Will a moment of anger make you lose what has taken long for you to build?

Such hard questions will eventually let calmness prevail. The fear of losing precious gains will bring calmness to maintain the status quo.

5. Selective Amnesia

Amnesia is a condition of forgetting things. The memory is compromised, and one forgets everything that happened in their lives. It is undesirable but maybe you should consider it if you want to be calm. Selective amnesia is choosing to willfully ignore the ugly things that have happened.

When you realize that something irritates you, shut it out of your life to regain sanity. Calmness is an expensive gift that should be treasured. Nothing should deprive you of the right to enjoy the serenity of life. Choose to look at the good side only of things. You can maintain calm by dwelling exclusively on it and refusing to give people the power to control you.

In conclusion, calmness is a trophy that should be on our shelves. These five ways to get calm are effective should we implement them correctly.

Chapter 8:

8 Bad Habits That Make You Age Faster

According to a statistic given in an article in Globe Newswire, it's projected that by the year 2019, the global anti-aging market will be worth 191.7 billion dollars! Clearly, a lot of people are investing in products and procedures to help keep themselves looking young and beautiful. But, as with any disease or condition, prevention is always far better than the cure, and the same holds true for anti-aging. Unfortunately, there is no magic fountain of youth that will keep you young forever. But there are some particular habits and mistakes that, when avoided, can make you less likely to need anti-aging products and procedures. If you're a person who is concerned about an aging appearance, it's going to be important to avoid the things that make you age faster!

1. Processed Foods

Foods that have been highly processed and refined not only lack the nutrients needed by the body to support proper functioning, they typically also contain synthetic chemicals and other harmful ingredients that are detrimental to health. These processed foods cause faster tissue breakdown and other cellular damage that leads to faster aging. Additionally, when the nutrients that the bodily tissues need to function optimally are not optimally supplied, both the function and appearance of the skin and other organs can suffer.

2. Smoking

Smoking is a habit that not only wreaks havoc on your health but certainly speeds up the aging process. Even smoking one cigarette causes a huge amount of oxidative stress. This oxidative stress causes wear and tear on the body's cells, causing many issues such as aging, wrinkles, and other forms of degeneration.

3. Drug Abuse

Too much drug use of any kind causes internal stress on the body that again causes dysfunction, breakdown, and lack of optimal functioning. Depending on the drug, some can cause water loss, loss of healthy fat tissue, toxicity and more that can leave you looking older and frailer.

4. Lack Of Hydration

Being improperly hydrated, especially chronically, surprisingly can make you look more aged. Water is essential for so many roles in the body that without enough of it, the function of the body suffers, which both directly and indirectly, can lead to quicker aging. Water gives your skin the soft, plump, vibrant, moist look that indicates health and youthfulness. Additionally, it helps internally to flush out toxins that can cause acne, red eyes, bags under the eyes, puffiness, and other ailments that certainly don't scream youthfulness!

5. Not Getting Enough Sleep

Getting insufficient sleep is a major way to age yourself quite quickly! A chronic lack of sleep causes the body to shut down. Your eyes become bloodshot and red, baggy eyes, wrinkled skin, low energy, and many other symptoms that make anyone look older than they are! Sleep is so important both for health and for beauty that there's even the common saying, "I need my beauty sleep!"

6. Stress

Being chronically stressed is another habit that wreaks havoc internally. Stress typically is also associated with other habits that hasten the aging process. When stressed, people tend to sleep more poorly, eat more poorly, take more medications and drugs, and other such things that disrupt health and advance aging. Chronic stress keeps stress hormones elevated in the bloodstream constantly, which can have negative effects on the complexion of your skin, both the coloration and wrinkles, and causes red eyes, and an overall slumped, broken down and aged function and appearance. Having these stress hormones elevated chronically can lead to a number of health problems, the least of which is wrinkles and aging!

7.   Being Physically Inactive

Being inactive is a sure way of making your body look and feel older than it really is. Sedentary living typically causes you to have poor posture, become overweight, lethargic, and just plain droopy! Keeping your body moving and strong does a surprising amount for keeping you looking and feeling youthful from the inside out. Individuals who stay active as they get older typically age much better.

8.   Prolonged Exposure To UV Rays

Getting too much exposure to UV rays, either from being out in the sun unprotected too much or from tanning bed use, really causes a lot of damage to the skin, leading to wrinkles, sunspots and other damage that makes you look old.

By consistently maintaining a wholesome, natural, active lifestyle, you'll automatically be on a better track for avoiding fast aging. Following a diet of fresh, natural foods, being active, managing stress, and getting proper sleep can do leaps and bounds for helping you stay youthful!

Chapter 9:

Sleeping For Happiness

Picture a three-legged stool. Each leg symbolizes one of the most important things your body needs to stay healthy. One leg is good nutrition—eating whole foods, in reasonable portion sizes; the second represents physical activity—getting in some moderate-to-vigorous exercise on most days of the week. The third leg? Quality sleep, and enough of it. When we don't get good rest, we're more likely to become ill, gain weight and feel depressed, and our cognitive skills, including memory and reasoning, can suffer. In the worst cases, sleep deprivation can raise our risk for two major threats: type 2 diabetes and heart disease.

But when you do get an adequate amount of top-notch sleep (seven to nine hours a night is optimal for most adults, though sleep needs vary a lot and you may need more or less than that), the benefits across all aspects of your life—including your physical and emotional health, your relationships and your career—are powerful. Here are some of the benefits

You'll Help Your Brain; We simply don't have the maximum brainpower we need to function when we're pooped all the time. Sleep is the essential downtime that grey matter needs to consolidate memories, process emotions, and simply recharge to clearly focus the next day.

You'll Shine at Work; You might think that burning the midnight oil will help you get ahead, but sleep is essential if you want to bring your A-game to any job. Not only do you need a full night's sleep to be focused and productive, you also need to be rested and recharged to be creative at work.

Research shows that sleep (particularly REM, or the rapid-eye movement stages of sleep) is important for memory and that the dreaming may offer a crucial "incubation" period for the brain to process problems and come up with solutions. You'll Keep Your Genes in Good Working Order; Our genes tell our bodies—our cells, to be precise—exactly what to do, day in and day out. For genes to function properly, you need plenty of sleep.

A 2013 study at the University of Surrey found that chronic sleep deprivation (defined as less than six hours of sleep every night for just one week) affects the functioning of about three percent of genes. That may not sound like much, but it's actually hundreds of genes, including some that influence inflammation, immunity, and how we responses to stress.

Your Relationships Could Improve; Who hasn't felt snappish when feeling absolutely exhausted? Tapping into your natural kindness and patience is much harder to do when the energy tank is chronically on "empty." And, over time, that can take a toll on the people closest to you. When you're well-rested, though, it's easier to take a deep breath and act in a way that shows the caring, loving person you are.

Chapter 10:

Avoid The Dreaded Burnout

Do you often lack the energy to get on with any new task and feel sluggish throughout most of your day? Do you feel the burden of work that keeps getting piled up each day?

I know we all try our best to manage everything on our hands and try to bring out the best in us. But while doing so, we engage in too many things and ultimately, they take their toll.

It is becoming easier and easier every day where people have more work than ever on their hands. And their sole motive throughout life becomes, to find more and better ways of earning a better living. To find more things to be good and successful at.

We all have things on our hands to complete but let me tell you one thing. You won't be able to continue much longer if you keep with this burnout and exhaustion.

Our body is an engine, and it needs a way of cooling down and tuning. So, what's the first step you need to reduce burnout? You need to get the right amount of sleep.

There is this myth that you sleep one-third of your life, so you don't need an 8-hour sleep. You can easily do the same with four hours and use the other four for more work. Trust me, this is not a myth, it is a misconception about proven research. Your body organs deserve at least half the time of what they spend serving us.

We can refresh and better our focus and cognitive skills once we have a good night's sleep full of dreams.

Another thing that most of us avoid doing is to say No to anyone anytime. The thing is that we don't have any obligation to anyone unless we are bound by a contract of blood or law to do or say anything that anyone tells us to do. The more we feel obligated to anyone, the more we try to do to impress that person or entity with our efforts and conduct.

This attitude isn't healthy for any relation. Excess of anything has never brought any good to anyone. So don't give up everything on just one thing. Instead, try to devise a balance between things. Over-commitment is never a good idea.

The third and final thing I want you to do is to give up on certain things at certain times. You don't need to carry your phone or laptop with you all day. This only creates a distraction even when you don't need to be in that environment.

You don't need to train your subconscious to be always alert on your emails and notifications or any incoming calls all day long. But sometimes you just need to give up on these things and zone out of your repetitive daily life.

Doing your best doesn't always mean giving yourself all out. Sometimes the best productive thing you can do is to relax. And that, my friends, can help you climb every mountain without ever getting tired of trying t do the same trail.

Chapter 11:

9 Habits To Wake Up Early

Waking up early is a real struggle for many people. People are battling this friendly monster silently. Friendly because the temptation to snooze the alarm or turn it off completely when it rings in the morning is irresistible. Almost everyone can attest to cursing under their breath when they hear their alarm go off loudly in the morning.

Here are 9 habits that you should strive to incorporate into your life if you wish to make waking early a part of your routine:

1. Sleeping Early

It is simple – early to bed, early to rise. Retiring to bed early will give you enough time to exhaust your sleep. The average person ought to have at least 8 hours of sleep. Sleeping early will create more time for rest and enable you to wake up on time.

Since sleep is not ignorable, you may be embarrassed when you find yourself sleeping when attending a meeting, or when you are at work. Save yourself this shame by sleeping early to wake up earlier.

After a long day of vicissitudes, gift your body the pleasure of having a good night's rest. Create extra time for this by lying horizontally early enough.

2. Scheduling Your Plans For the Day Beforehand

A good plan is a job half done. Before the day ends, plan for the activities of the next day. When it is all mapped out, you will sleep with a clear mind on what you will be facing the next day. Planning is not a managerial routine task alone but everyone's duty of preparing to fight the unknown the following day.

Waking up early is a difficult decision to make impromptu because of the weakness in yielding to the temptation of 'sleeping for only five more minutes.' Having a plan gives you a reason to wake up early.

3. Creating Deadlines

Working under pressure is an alternative motivation for waking up early if planning has failed. With assignments to submit within a short time, or work reports to be submitted on short notice, the need to wake up early to beat these deadlines will be automatic.

We can create deadlines and ultimatums for ourselves without waiting on our superiors to impose them on us. This self-drive will last longer, and it will increase our productivity instead of waiting for our clients and employers to give us ultimatums.

4. Being Psychologically Prepared

The mind is the powerhouse of the body. Mental preparedness is the first step towards making and sticking to landmark decisions. The mind should initiate and accept the idea of waking up early before you can comfortably adopt this new routine.

Develop a positive attitude towards rising early and all other subsequent results will fall in place. The first person you need to convince to move towards a particular cause is you. As simple as waking up early seems, many people are grappling with late coming.

This is fixable by making a conscious decision to turn around your sleeping habits. The greatest battle is fought in the mind, where the body antagonizes the spirit.

5. Finding Like-Minded Friends

Birds of the same feathers flock together. When you are in the company of friends with one routine, your habits are fortified. With no dissenting voice amongst your friends to discourage you from waking up early, your morning routine will find a permanent spot in your life.

The contrary is true. When you are the odd one out in a clique of friends who have no regard for time, you are likely to lose even the little time-consciousness you had. They will contaminate you with their habits and before you know it, you will slip back to your old self (an over sleeper).

When you also decide to be a loner and not associate with those with the same habits as yourself, then you risk giving up on the way. The psych from friends will be lacking and soon you will just revert to your old habits.

When you want to walk fast, walk alone. When you want to go far, walk with others.

6. Being Sensitive To Your Environment

It takes a man of understanding to read and understand the prevailing times and seasons. You may occasionally visit a friend or a relative and spend the night. How can you wake up way past sunrise in a foreign environment? This will suggest to your hosts that you are lazy.

Create a good image by waking up a little bit early. If allowed, help do some morning chores over there.

Adjust your routine accordingly. Win over people by waking up early to join them in their morning chores. It is there where friendships are forged. A simple habit of waking up early can be an avenue to make alliances.

7. Addressing Any Health Issues Early

In case of any underlying health conditions that can stop you from waking up early in the morning, seek medical help fast. You may be willing to be an early riser but may be suffering from asthma triggered by the chilly weather in the morning.

When that condition is controlled, you can also manage to wake up a little bit earlier than before and engage in health-friendly activities in the morning. It is a win-win. In either case, going for a medical check-up frequently will keep you healthy to wake up early.

Your health is a priority and when taken care of you will wake up early.

8. It Is a Habit for the Successful

Ironically, those who have made it in life wake up earlier than the less established ones. One would think that it is the place of the less-founded ones to rise early to go to work and do business so that they can be at par with the wealthy and mighty. Instead, the reverse is true.

Follow the footsteps of great leaders who wake up early to attend to their affairs. They have become who they are because they give no room to the laziness of waking up late. We all have 24 hours in a day to do our businesses, where does the gap between the haves and the have-nots come from? That gap comes from how we use our time.

9. Having a Cheerful Spirit

A cheerful spirit finds joy in even what seems trivial. You should not see waking up early as punishment. It should be a routine to be followed happily religiously. When you have a cheerful spirit, knowing for whose benefit you rise early, then it will be a habit engraved into your spirit.

The above 9 habits to wake up early are key to discovering our purpose and build a new routine henceforth of being an early riser. The most successful people in the world abide by this routine so why not make it yours too.

•

Chapter 12:

How To Become A Morning Person

Our natural sleep/wake cycles are known as our circadian rhythm, and they can vary a lot from person to person. People fall into different groups, or chronotypes, depending on whether they feel most awake and alert in the morning, in the evening or somewhere in between.

No chronotype is inherently better or worse than another. There's nothing wrong with staying up late and sleeping in. "If that schedule fits with your lifestyle and your obligations, it's not necessary to change it."

The trouble comes when your late bedtime clashes with your early morning obligations. If you're regularly getting less than the recommended seven to nine hours of sleep a night, your health and well-being can suffer.

Unfortunately, we can't pick our chronotypes. Genetics plays a part in whether you identify as a night owl or a morning lark. Still, your habits and behaviours can reinforce those natural tendencies. And those habits aren't set in stone. "By making behavioural changes, you may be able to shift your sleep schedule preferences,"

How to reset your circadian rhythm? How, exactly, do you become more of a morning person?

Shift your bedtime: Count back from the time your alarm rings, aiming for a total of seven to nine hours a night. That will be your target bedtime — eventually. If you're used to turning in well after midnight, willing yourself to suddenly fall asleep at 10:00 p.m. is sure to backfire.

Aim to go to bed 15 or 20 minutes earlier than usual for a few days. Then push it back another 15 minutes for several more days. "It's important to adjust your sleep time gradually," she says.

Make it routine: A quiet bedtime routine is key to helping you fall asleep earlier. At least an hour before lights out, dim the lights and power down your electronics. Find something soothing to do, like taking a warm bath, reading a book or listening to a (not-too-stimulating) podcast. "Give yourself time to wind down and prepare your mind for bed."

Lighten up: "Our circadian rhythms are responsive to light and dark," Exposure to bright light first thing in the morning helps you feel more alert and also helps shift your internal rhythm toward an earlier wake time.

Natural light is the best, so get outside or open your bedroom window. If you can't get outside or your room is natural light-deprived, try a light therapy lamp that mimics the spectrum of natural light.

Make mornings more pleasant: Try to schedule something to look forward to in the morning so that getting up feels like less of a slog. Perhaps a hot cup of coffee, sipped in silence, and the daily crossword puzzle. Knowing that something pleasant awaits can help you take that first, painful step out of bed.

Move your alarm clock: Hitting snooze is all too tempting, so remove that option. Try putting your alarm clock across the room, so you have to get up to turn it off.

Some apps make it even harder to sleep in, by forcing you to engage in mentally stimulating activities like solving a puzzle to stop the beeping. "Do whatever works to keep you from hitting snooze,"

Chapter 13:

Stop Hitting That Snooze Button

Life is about the things you can take control of. You live your life day by day. So, every day in your life is a small part that starts with you waking up and ends with you going back to bed. You sleep every night after setting up at least five different alarms. Why do you set all these alarms and then sleep until the last? It is simple; You set these alarms because there have been tasks on your mind that you must do.

You set more than one alarm because you know you will snooze them all for sure. You can't get up on the first alarm because you are too lazy and you don't have any discipline in your life. Your alarm keeps buzzing, and you wait till the last ring to either snooze it or for it to end. But this is your deciding moment. This is your time to decide if you want to get up or keep snoozing as you have been avoiding and snoozing opportunities your whole life.

This is a battle with yourself to test if you will hit the snooze or if you will get up and do what is necessary. You set alarms to help you get up when the natural causes are not enough. You might be a deep sleeper or a light sleeper, but you need some aid or reminder to get up in the morning. But when you hit that snooze button, you have essentially broken the determination with which you set that alarm last night.

Maybe this was your last chance to succeed. Perhaps this was your last chance to get out of this state of depression and laziness. You aren't probably the guy who promotes success on one's own actions. You can't even handle an alarm on your phone; how do you plan to take the world's mockery when you fail at other things in your life.

If you train yourself to be subconsciously active even before you hear the first alarm, this means you are well equipped to break your sleep cycles whenever you want. This mirrors your dedication to your work and your control over your own body.

If you don't hit the snooze button and go out to work, it will not matter too much if you fail out there. Why? Because now you started your day with success when you acted against your wishes to sleep a little longer and didn't hit that snooze button. Now you are on a power curve, and you feel good about the following things because now you are hopeful. Because now you know you can bring a change within yourself.

When you didn't hit that snooze button, you showed yourself how much this day means to you and how much of a promising character you are. Life is long enough to hit the snooze some other time, but for now, you need to seize the day as it might never be like this again.

Chapter 14:

Start Each Day Stress-Free

Getting up in the morning with a blank mind, not knowing what to do. Trying to figure out how to cope with what happened yesterday. We all go through this, right?

But today is an important day and you aren't prepared for it. It stresses us out. It's the first thing we do in the morning, without realizing the impact it'll have on our day.

The entire day will be tainted with negative vibes and worries if you are stressed out in the morning. Your brain will accept that nothing will go right, and you will not be able to accomplish anything. And so you quit. We stress over things without even trying. You cannot control your source of stress, but you can manage the tension that is making you feel stressed.

Let us take an example. How heavy is a glass of water? About 10-12 ounces. Then if you hold this glass of water for a minute, you will not feel any harm, but in an hour, you will feel pain in your arm, in two hours, your arm will go numb, and in a day, your arm might paralyze. It wasn't the weight of the glass, but how long you held it.

The stress is like this glass. No matter how big or how small the stress is, the longer you hold onto it, the more damage it causes.

Therefore, it is important to start each day stress-free to feel optimism, good vibes, and happiness the whole day. I will tell you how you can start each day unstressed and full of motivation. The first thing you need to do is make sure you sleep well. Even if you are fully prepared, you will end up stressed out if you don't get enough sleep.

Make a to-do list of things you need to do tomorrow, so you wake up every morning knowing what are your today's priorities. Prepare yourself for the next day's activities the night before. Let us say you have an important meeting, set an early alarm, prepare your presentation, keep all your important notes and files on your desk, decide what to wear, etc. Stay calm and know you can handle it. This way you will feel less stressed on your important day.

Suppose you have less than 30 minutes left for an important exam. There are a few questions left. You start stressing about finishing it. You know the answers, but you are worried about time. This stress will trigger the body's "flight or fight" response. You will start sweating, your heart will start beating quickly, your brain will stop responding. Finally, you will decide to skip it and rely on what you have already done.

This is what stress does to you, even if you are well prepared for everything. In contrast, if you have remained calm and believed you can do it, you will for sure have completed your test earlier and much more efficiently than you would have otherwise.

Keep in mind that stress doesn't ease your pain or lighten your burden; it just makes things worse. Motivate yourself to achieve today's goal by starting the day with positive energy. It is very important for you to be happy and stress-free in the morning to stay calm and relaxed throughout the day. Try meditation, yoga, morning walk, or whatever makes you stress-free at the start of the day. Don't be so hard on yourself, have confidence and faith in yourself.

Chapter 15:

Getting Rid Of Tiredness After Waking Up Early

Waking up early goes beyond getting out of bed before everyone else. It is some sort of a ritual that must be observed by those who want to make it in life. However, the common obstacle that most people face is that they feel tired for the rest of the day after they wake up early. This is not the ideal result that should be experienced. You should feel energetic throughout the day. This is how you can avoid fatigue throughout the day after waking up early:

1. Proper Preparation

As highlighted earlier, waking up early is not an act but a routine. This requires mental, emotional, and physical preparation. As you go to bed, your mind must be prepared to be awake the following morning at the time of your choice. Doing this repeatedly will turn on a switch in your mind and you will be sleepless at the appointed time to wake up.

Understandably, some people are insomniacs, and this makes them wake up early. If they had a choice, they would sleep to their satisfaction. They may feel tired throughout the day because they did not have enough resting time the previous night. Your emotions are in sync with your mind. When your mind is prepped to be up at a specified time the following day, you will spend your day excellently.

2. Freshen Up

What do you do when you wake up? Maybe you unlock your phone and check the notifications you may have received overnight. This is bad practice. Prioritize taking a warm or cold shower immediately after waking up. This will make you alert, and you will not return to sleep that morning. After a shower, change into other clothes. Do not remain in your nightdress or pajamas. It will encourage you to return to bed. It does not matter whether or not you have plans to leave the house. When you are dressed in other clothes, you will not have sleep syndrome or feel tired for nothing during the day.

3. Be Active

What are the activities lined up for you during the day? What you do after waking up matters a lot. If possible, avoid staying back in your bedroom. Go to the study room, living room, or the gym and find something to do. The kind of activities you engage in will either leave you energetic or drained.

It is not to imply that you should only do intensive activities. They will make you feel tired. The point is not to be idle. When your mind registers it, you will feel tired even without doing anything. Observe how active people start their days. Do they complain of fatigue throughout the day? They will only feel exhaustion at the end of the day.

4.   Plan Out Your Activities Successively

The reason you feel tired throughout the day when you wake up early is that you have not planned your day properly. You should always know what will follow after you have finished one task. You will work throughout your day like programmed software. Knowing the beginning and end will hardly make you feel tired unlike when things are unclear. You should have a vision of what the end looks like. Although you may be exhausted, the sight of the end will empower you to keep moving.

5.   Take a Break When Necessary

Learn to reward yourself with breaks in-between your day. You will eventually break down after starting your day early. Breaks do not mean you are lazy. They will help you recover your energy and when you resume, it will be as if you were never tired. Waking up early means doing a lot more things than other people have done. You will feel tired, but you will be more productive than a majority of people. Remember to take lots of water too during the breaks.

Conclusion

Waking up early does not exempt you from feeling tired. But with these five steps, you can optimize the advantage you have of waking up early and feeling less tired throughout the day.

Chapter 16:

How To Worry Less

How many of you worry about little things that affect the way you go about your day? That when you're out with your friends having a good time or just carrying out your daily activities, when out of nowhere a sudden burst of sadness enters your heart and mind and immediately you start to think about the worries and troubles you are facing. It is like you're fighting to stay positive and just enjoy your day, but your mind just won't let you. It becomes a tug of war or a battle to see who wins?

How many of you also lose sleep because your mind starts racing at bedtime and you're flooded with sad feelings of uncertainty, despair, worthlessness or other negative emotions that when you wake up, that feeling of dread immediately overwhelms you and you just feel like life is too difficult and you just don't want to get out of bed.

Well, If you have felt those things or are feeling those things right now, I want to tell you you're not alone. Because I too struggle with those feelings or emotions on a regular basis.

At the time of writing this, I was faced with many uncertainties in life. My business had just ran into some problems, my stocks weren't doing well, I had lost money, my bank account was telling me I wasn't good enough, but most importantly, i had lost confidence. I had lost the ability to face each day with confidence that things will get better. I felt that I was worthless and that bad things will always happen to me. I kept seeing the negative side of things and it took a great deal of emotional toll on me. It wasn't like i chose to think and feel these things, but they just came into my mind whenever they liked. It was like a parasite feeding off my negative energy and thriving on it and weakening me at the same time.

Now your struggles may be different. You may have a totally different set of circumstances and struggles that you're facing, but the underlying issue is the same. We all go through times of despair, worry, frustration, and uncertainty. And it's totally normal and we shouldn't feel ashamed of it but to accept that it is a part of life and part of our reality.

But there are things we can do to minimize these worries and to shift to a healthier thought pattern that increases our ability to fight off these negative emotions.

I want to give you 5 actionable steps that you can take to worry less and be happier. And these steps are interlinked that can be carried out in fluid succession for the greatest benefit to you. But of course, you can choose whichever ones speaks the most to you and it is more important that you are able to practice any one of these steps consistently rather than doing all 5 of them haphazardly. But I want to make sure I give you all the tools so that you can make the best decisions for yourself.

Try this with me right now as I go through these 5 steps and experience the benefit for yourself instead of waiting until something bad happens.

The very first step is simple. Just breathe. When a terrible feeling of sadness rushes into your body out of nowhere, take that as a cue to close your eyes, stop whatever you are doing, and take 5 deep breathes through your nose. Breathing into your chest and diaphragm. Deep breathing has the physiological benefit of calming your nerves and releasing tension in the body and it is a quick way to block out your negative thoughts. Pause the video if you need to do practice your deep breathing before we move on.

And as you deep breathe, begin the second step. Which is to practice gratefulness. Be grateful for what you already have instead of what you think u need to have to be happy. You could be grateful for your dog, your family, your friends, and whatever means the most to you. And if you cannot think of anything to be grateful for, just be grateful that you are even alive and walking on this earth today because that is special and amazing in its own right.

Next is to practice love and kindness to yourself. You are too special and too important to be so cruel to yourself. You deserve to be loved and you owe it to yourself to be kind and forgiving. Life is tough as it is, don't make it harder. If you don't believe in yourself, I believe in you and I believe in your worthiness as a person that you have a lot left to give.

The fourth step is to Live Everyday as if it were your last. Ask yourself, will you still want to spend your time worrying about things out of your control if it was your last day on earth? Will you be able to forgive yourself if you spent 23 out of the last 24 hours of your life worrying? Or will you choose to make the most out of the day by doing things that are meaningful and to practice love to your family, friends, and yourself?

Finally, I just want you to believe in yourself and Have hope that whatever actions you are taking now will bear fruition in the future. That they will not be in vain. That at the end of the day, you have done everything to the very best of your ability and you will have no regrets and you have left no stone unturned.

How do you feel now? Do you feel that it has helped at least a little or even a lot in shaping how you view things now? That you can shift your perspective and focus on the positives instead of the worries?

If it has worked for you today, I want to challenge you to consistently practice as many of these 5 steps throughout your daily lives every single day. When you feel a deep sadness coming over you, come back to this video if you need guidance, or practice these steps if you remember them on your own.

Chapter 17:

You're Good Enough

People come and say 'I did something stupid today. I am so bad at this. Why is it always me?' You will acknowledge even if no one else says it, we often say it to ourselves.

So what if we did something stupid or somewhat a little awkward. I am sure no one tries to do such things voluntarily. Things happen and sometimes we cause them because we have a tendency to go out of our way sometimes. Or sometimes our ways have a possibility of making things strange.

It doesn't make you look stupid or dumb or ugly or less competent. These are the things you make up of yourself. I am not saying people don't judge. They do. But their judgment should not make you think less of yourself.

No matter how much you slip up, you must not stop, and you must not bow down to some critique. You only have to be a little determined and content with yourself that you have got it alright.

You need to realize your true potential because no matter what anyone says, you have what it takes to get to the top.

Need some proof? Ask yourself, have you had a full belly today? Have you had a good night's sleep last night? Have you had the will and energy to get up and appear for your job and duties? Have you had the guts to ask someone out to dinner because you had a crush on them?

If you have a good answer to any of these questions, and you have done it all on your own with your efforts. Congratulations my friend, you are ready to appraise yourself.

You have now come to terms with your abilities, and you don't need anyone else's approval or appraisal. You don't depend on anyone either psychologically or emotionally.

So now when the times get tough you can remind yourself that you went through it before. And even if you failed back then, you have the right energy and right state of mind to get on top of it now. You are now well equipped to get ahead of things and be a better person than you were the last time.

You are enough for everything good or not so good happening in and around you.

Your health, your relations, your carrier, your future. Everything can be good and better when you have straightened out your relationship with yourself. When you have found ways to talk to yourself ad make yourself realize your true importance. When you learn to admire yourself.

Once you learn to be your best critic, you can achieve anything. Without ever second-guessing yourself and ever trying to care for what anyone else will think.

If you find yourself in a position where you had your heart broken but you still kept it open, you should have a smile on your face. Because now you might be on your path to becoming a superior human being.

Chapter 18:

When It's Okay to Not Be Okay

Let's be honest, happiness is not something you can "just choose". If it was, then sad moments could not be there. Do not pressure yourself to be happy, because if you do, then you are inadvertently setting a path of the war with yourself. This is why adopting a mindset that embraces "not all that happy" feelings we can arise within us is essential for carrying on with a happier life.

In the stumbling on happiness, Daniel Gilbert describes happiness, "There is no basic recipe for happiness." Certainly, it's anything but an objective to accomplish. Or maybe it's the bi-result of carrying on with a wholehearted life - a daily existence wherein we permit ourselves to chance feel the full range of human feeling - dissatisfaction, grief, dismissal, misery, insufficiency - and to accept our battles and to acknowledge our ourselves as the questionable "human becoming" that we are".

We can help ourselves along in that cycle by accomplishing a greater amount of what grows our ability for every one of the encounters and feelings that life holds available.

Here are a 7 Ways To help You Cope and Accept When It's Okay Not to Be Okay.

1. Accept Life's Upsetting Emotions

Bear this in mind, there are only two types of people who don't usually experience painful emotions; psychopaths and people who've died. Feeling or experiencing sad and painful moments are part and parcel of your life. At any point when you deny, excuse, numb or attempt to obstruct yourself from feeling them completely – something many are profoundly adroit at doing – you are just prolonging your torment and making superfluous suffering.

2. Practice "Gently/Friendly Curiosity"

As human beings, the truth is, we are intrinsically emotional or passionate creatures– occasionally, we act before reasoning. Also, satisfaction – those sentiments bliss, happiness, and connection - is only one of the numerous feelings on the wide enthusiastic range.

The best way to encounter unadulterated snapshots of happiness, connection, appreciation, and love is the point at which you allow yourself to experience sadness, misery, dread, and hurt. Embrace these sad feelings with curiosity. This requires allowing yourself to sit with the less lovely feelings without desensitizing, minimizing, or over-relating to them. As such, "the solitary way out is through."

3. Practice More of Whatever Makes You Stronger – Body, Mind, and Soul

Since numerous things in your life are out of your control, it bodes well to be proactive in those parts of your life over which we have some proportion of control. Growing day by day customs and propensities to assist you with bringing your "best self" to your greatest difficulties is vital. Eat well, burn some calories, invest your energy with individuals who lift you. Limit time with the individuals who don't. Re-energize your energy, re-focus your soul, and pull together on your first concerns. The little private every day moves you make can lead to large open outcomes that you frequently need.

4. Look at Yourself as a Person Who Is "Human Becoming"

Every time you will see people who seem to have everything in perfect order and feel they don't encounter any of the battles and uncertainties that you do. It's untrue.

Accepting yourself as a 'human becoming that you are – complete with every one of your inadequacies, fears, and frailty – helps you to grow fully into your humankind and connect all more with that of others.

Everyone at some point in their lives messes up, falls down and up, and fails to be as kind-hopeful patient-restrained as they'd prefer to be. Such is the human condition. Thumping yourself for being human doesn't serve you. This is the reason, in your fallen moments, you should be kinder to yourself. Commit to accepting your flaws or imperfections and acknowledge your mistakes as you move up to healing.

5. Rest Your Sadness

Thinking of sadness as the opposite of happiness is easy, and accordingly, something to be evaded. Truth be told, misery is the feeling that directs you toward what you care about most and is a pathway to happiness. At the point when you cut yourself off from feeling the profundity of your misfortune, from sitting with your misery and distress, you additionally cut yourself off from being available to bliss, close connection, and happiness.

Therefore, allowing yourself ample time to sit with your sadness, let the tears flow-if need be, and be there fully to feel the sad moments-that permitting yourself to fully feel the ache -taking all things together in its rawness - allows you to gradually discover your way back wholly and healing and to getting more deliberate in your work, as a parent, and throughout everyday life. It's an excursion that is continuous.

6. Cultivate Seeds of Gratitude

Happiness cannot be bought from external sources, be it money, success, and fame. It is all on everyone's knowledge that most people who are materially wealthy are profoundly unhappy. Which is true. You should learn to appreciate whatever you have, hence the more appreciation, the happier you will feel. It's the reason we must be purposeful in zeroing in on the things that fuel feelings of appreciation, in any event, when there are parts of our lives that aren't as we'd like.

7. Spend Your Time Offline-take a Break From Social Media

Finally, perhaps the main thing you can do to cultivate happiness and develop your versatility for managing your afflictions is being in a place where there are meaningful relationships. Turning to the right people and connecting with them in realness and during your vulnerable moments is more impactful on your inner peace instead of scrolling down the social media feeds.

In conclusion, it is okay to be vulnerable- it is okay to feel unhappy-it is okay to share the feeling with the right people. Just keep in mind that an unhappy feeling which is felt enough can permanently reside in your psyche and overshadow all others. So, feel what should be felt and afterward be deliberate in investing your time and attention toward whatever re-establishes viewpoint and grows your ability to make a move to make whatever it is you need a greater amount of in your life.

Chapter 19:

Dealing With Worries

Everyone worries from time to time. Too much worry can be bad as it leaves us feeling tense and anxious. Even though we might say to ourselves and others – "Stop worrying. It's pointless. It won't do any good" – there is something about worrying that makes it hard to stop. This is because worry can be helpful.

Useful worry prompts action. All other worry is pointless.

Worry is useful if it makes you pay attention

Worrying about the weather cannot stop it raining on your washing; however, if you watch the sky and act to bring in your washing when it rains, being aware that it will have helped.

Worry is useful, provided it is turned into a plan for action

For example, worrying that your electricity might get cut off might lead you to act to pay your bill on time. Once the bill has been paid, the worrying would stop, and you would feel better.

·Worry is useful if it helps you be better prepared

Worry may help you think about "what you could do if...," or "what would happen if...". Worrying "what would happen if my house was burgled" could make you act to take out house insurance and lock your front door when you go out.

Worry Without Action Does Nothing

I worry on its own did something then we could worry all day to increase our bank balance. On the other hand taking action such as selling something, working more hours, or spending less will directly affect our bank balance.

Is it Worth Worrying About?

Four things are not worth worrying about, but that account for many of our worries: the unimportant, the unlikely, the uncertain, and the uncontrollable. Ban these from your life, and you will worry less.

The Unimportant

It is easy to fill your life with worries about little things. When you find yourself worrying, start to question yourself instead. Ask yourself, "How important is the thing that I am worried about?"

Here are three points to help you answer this question.

1. The Five-Year Rule

Ask yourself: "will this matter in 5 years?" This is a way of looking at your worry from a long-term point of view. View your worries differently: will this still be a concern in a week, a month, or a year?

2. The Measuring Rod

Ask yourself: "Where, on a scale of bad experiences, is the thing I'm worried about?" Think about a very bad experience you have had. How does your current worry feel when compared with this?

3. The Calculator

Ask yourself: "How much worry is this worth?" We only have a certain amount of time and energy. Make sure you do not spend more worry on your problem than it is worth. You need your time and energy for more important things. Maybe some time you would have spent worrying could be used for doing something.

Chapter 20:

Discovering Your Purpose

If you guys don't already know, this is one of the topics that I really love talking about. And I never get tired of it. Having a purpose is something that I always believe everyone should have. Having a purpose to live, to breathe, to get up each day, I believe that without purpose, there is no point to life.

So today we're going to talk about how to discover your purpose, and why you should make it a point to find one if you didn't already start looking.

So what is purpose exactly. A purpose is a reason to do something. Is to have something else greater than ourselves to work for. You see, I believe if we are only focused on ourselves, instead of others, we will not be able to be truly happy in life. Feeding our own self-interests does not bring us joy as one might think. After living the life that I had, I realized that true happiness only comes when you bring joy to someone else's life. Whether it be helping others professionally or out of selflessness, this happiness will radiate and reflect back to us from someone else who is appreciative of your efforts.

On some level, we can look into ourselves to be happy. For example, being grateful for life, loving ourselves, and all that good stuff. Yes, keep doing those things. But there is a whole other dimension if we devote our time and energy into helping others once we have already conquered ourselves. If you look at many of the most successful people on the planet, after they have acquired an immense amount of wealth, many of them look to passion projects or even philanthropy where they can give back to the community when having more money doesn't do anything for them anymore. If you look at Elon Musk and Jeff Bezos, these two have a greater purpose which is their space projects. Where they visualize humans being able to move out of Earth one day where civilization is able to expand. Or Bill Gates and Warren Buffet, who have pledged to give billions of their money away for philanthropic work, to help the less fortunate and to fund organizations that work towards finding cures to diseases.

Now for us mere mortals, we don't need to think so big. Our purpose need not be so extravagant. It can be as simple as having a purpose to provide for your loved one, to work hard to bring your family members of holidays and travel, or to bring joy to your elderly relatives by organizing activities for them to do. There is no purpose that is too big or too small.

Your purpose could be helping others find a beautiful home, doing charitable work, or even feeding and providing for your growing family.

As humans, we will automatically work harder if we have a clear and defined purpose. We have a reason to get up each day, to go to work, to earn that paycheck, so that we can spend it on things and people, even ourselves at times. Without a purpose, we struggle to find meaning in the work that we do. We struggle to see the big picture and we find that we have no reason to work so hard, or even at all. And we struggle to find life worth living.

This revelation came to me when I started seeing my work as helping some other person in a meaningful way. Where my work was not just about making money to buy nice things, but to be able to impact someone else's life in a positive way. That became my purpose. To see them learn something new, and to bring a joy and smile to their faces. That thought that I was contributing something useful to someone made me smile more than money ever could. Yes, money can help you live a comfortable life, but helping others can go a much farther way into giving your life true purpose.

So, I challenge each and every one of you to find a purpose in everything that you do, and if you struggle to find one, start by making the goal to help others a priority. Think of the difference you can make to others and that could very well be your purpose in life as well.

Chapter 21:

Don't Overthink Things

Analysis Paralysis, how many of you have heard of this term before? When a decision is placed before us, many of us try to weigh the pros and cons, over and over again, day and night, and never seem to be able to come up with an answer, not even one week later.

I have been guilty of doing such a thing many times in my life, in fact many in the past month alone. What I've come to realize is that there is never going to be a right decision, but that things always work out in the end as long as it is not a rash decision.

Giving careful thought to any big decision is definitely justified. From buying a car, to a house, to moving to another state or country for work, these are big life-changing decisions that could set the course for our professional and financial future for years to come. In these instances, it is okay to take as much time as we need to settle on the right calculated choice for us. Sometimes in these situations, we may not know the right answer as well, but we take a leap of faith and hope for the best and that is the only thing we can do. And that is perfectly okay.

But if we translate the time and effort, we take in those big projects into daily decisions such as where to go, what to eat, or who to call, we will find ourselves in a terrible predicament multiple times a day. If we overthink the simple things, life just becomes so much more complicated. We end up over-taxing our brain to the point where it does not have much juice left to do other things that are truly important.

The goal is to keep things simple by either limiting your choices or by simply going with your gut. Instead of weighing every single pro and con before making a decision, just go. The amount of time we waste calculating could be better spent into energy for other resources.

I have found that i rarely ever make a right choice even after debating hours on end whether I should go somewhere. Because i would always wonder what if i had gone to the other place instead. The human mind is very funny thing. We always seem to think the grass could be greener on the other side, and so we are never contented with what we have in front of us right here right now.

The next time you are faced with a non-life changing decision, simply flip a coin and just go with the one that the coin has chosen for you. Don't look back and flip the coin the other way unless it is truly what your heart wants. We will never be truly happy with every single choice we make. We can only make the most of it.

Chapter 22:

Enjoying The Simple Things

Today we're going to talk about a topic that might sound cheesy, but trust me it's worth taking a closer look at. And that is how we should strive to enjoy the simple things in life.

Many of us think we need a jam-packed schedule for the week, month, or year, to tell us that we are leading a very productive and purposeful life. We find ways to fill our time with a hundred different activities. Going to this event, that event, never slowing down. And we find ourselves maybe slightly burnt out by the end of it.

We forget that sometimes simplicity is better than complication. Have you sat down with your family for a simple lunch meal lately? You don't have to talk, you just have to be in each other's company and enjoying the food that is being served in front of you.

I found myself appreciating these moments more than I did running around to activities thinking that I needed something big to be worth my time. I found sitting next to my family on the couch watching my own shows while they watch theirs very rewarding. I found eating alone at my favourite restaurant while watching my favourite sitcom to be equally as enjoyable as hanging out with a group of 10 friends. I also found myself richly enjoying a long warm shower every morning and evening. It is the highlights of my day.

My point is that we need to start looking at the small things we can do each day that will bring us joy. Things that are within our control. Things that we know can hardly go wrong. This will provide some stability to gain some pleasure from. The little nuggets in the day that will not be determined by external factors such as the weather, friends bailing on us, or irritating customers.

When we focus on the little things, we make life that much better to live through.

Chapter 23:

Five Daily Positive Thoughts

Positive Thoughts

In simple terms, positive thoughts are about good things. They are ever progressive. They reflect on possibility and success. In the world of positivity, the impossible is non-existent. It is just a state of rest. You live to try your chance another day.

Positive thoughts are powerful instruments. A man is a product of his thoughts. A defeated mind will always yield defeat. You cannot become what you do not think of. Your thoughts are a reflection of your desires. You only think of what your heart craves, and you find ways to satisfy that desire.

The Battle of Armageddon

A battle is won starting from the mind. Yes, physical fitness and swiftness also count, but all that is useless if your mind is not psyched for victory.

When soldiers go to war, they psyche each other up and talk of only how they will subdue the enemy. In fact, the military doctor must approve your mental and physical fitness before deployment.

You can neither have a pessimistic fellow in your battalion nor a suicidal comrade as your partner as you go to war. They are a liability.

Similarly, it is important to have positive thoughts throughout no matter how tough life gets. Even at the brink of giving up, never quit. Just rest.

Here are five powerful positive thoughts you should have daily:

1. What A Beautiful Day!

Are you glad to see another day or do you curse it? Your thoughts in the morning determine what your day will look like.

The first thing that you should think of is – what a beautiful day!

This thought psyches you up for what is ahead, both the good and bad. Although it is impossible to know what lies ahead, hope that everything will be fine. Do not recall yesterday's bad events. Consider it as just a bad day that will soon be forgotten.

Start the day radiating positivity and love all the way!

2. It Is Possible!

It does not matter who says it's impossible, you should always think of the possible. You are a product of your thoughts. Always be positive about success and it shall come your way.

A lot of things happen during the day. Things that you had not even planned for. This is normal because there are many variables at play. Do not let that scare you into giving up.

Be armed with thoughts of positivity and how you are going to meet your targets. Set your eyes on the target you are aiming for and nothing else.

You will thank yourself for it!

3. I Shall Overcome!

Well, sometimes you feel that the world is against you. Everything is moving in the opposite direction and you can almost taste defeat.

This thought should be permanently in your mind – You shall overcome!

Make it your habit to declare victory over challenges. Confess it aloud if you have to. Speak boldly to those you meet.

When thoughts of victory occupy your mind, your body and soul work towards that. This is how you can fight the whispers in your ears preaching the gospel of failure.

It is never too late to declare victory!

4. I Am The Best!

You are the best. Have confident thoughts in your mind and believe in your ability to face whatever comes in your way head-on.

Confident thoughts will boost your self-esteem. Say to yourself albeit silently, "I am strong!"

If anyone should clap for you, it has to be you. Let others come join the bandwagon.

You are in competition with YOU!

5. I Shall Learn!

As you work through your day, you may come across things that you do not know so well. Take it as a learning point. Never despise yourself.

Tell yourself that you shall learn. There is nothing under the sun that you cannot understand if you set your heart to it.

It is never failure but a LESSON!

These five daily positive thoughts are important to keep you going. Be the person you will be proud of.

Chapter 24:

Follow Your Heart

We spend most of our lives trying to follow our heads and ignore what our hearts say. We set practical, monetary, and professional goals, but how long until we realize that we also need to set goals to follow our hearts. We push ourselves harder and harder while trying to live in our heads. Real growth isn't trying to prove yourself to your boss, your family, friends, or the world, and rather it starts when you focus on proving that you are good enough and content enough for yourself. Once in a while, you can follow your heart and show those that matter to you that you care about them instead of working long hours, getting ahead, and making the bottom line.

When we start to follow our hearts, we cease having regrets. It doesn't matter if things go in our favor or against it; what matters is at least we tried and listened to our hearts. We would be honest to ourselves and won't be asking "what if" for the rest of our lives. We would gradually start to trust our instincts and know that our hearts would always guide us in the right direction. Even if it doesn't, we wouldn't have any regrets.

We start to respect ourselves and begin to gain respect and admiration from the people around us when we follow our hearts. It happens because we come out in a clear light, free from all the negativities and meaningless things. We focus on the good and positive that fill us with passion and purpose and give importance to what matters most.

When we start to follow our hearts, we might get to know ourselves on a level we have never before. We will ask ourselves the tough questions about what matters to us. It would be surprising to many of us how deeply we would start to analyze ourselves. It's sometimes very difficult to choose between our heart and mind, but if we follow our heart, we can always find ways to make our heart's desire come to fruition. We can also ask ourselves if we are on the right and genuine path. Our hearts are most restless when we tend to go off course. So, listen to your heart. It might tell you all the secrets.

Our hearts are the most beautiful and selfless organs of our bodies. Following the intuitions of your heart will surely ensure that we love ourselves and we love others as well. It will tell you to forgive those who have wronged us so that we would be at peace with ourselves. Having a firm faith and belief that our hearts would say the right thing to do would make us survive so many situations.

It is essential to listen and follow your heart because it knows your deepest and truest desires. It knows your wants and needs and how to make them genuinely fulfilled. When we are honest towards our hearts, we become open to ourselves and focus on being bigger and better.

Chapter 25:

How To Rid Yourself of Distraction

Distraction and disaster sound rather similar.

It is a worldwide disorder that you are probably suffering from.

Distraction is robbing you of precious time during the day.

Distraction is robbing you of time that you should be working on your goals.

If you don't rid yourself of distraction, you are in big trouble.

It is a phenomenon that most employees are only productive 3 out of 8 hours at the office.

If you could half your distractions, you could double your productivity.

How far are you willing to go to combat distraction?

How badly do you want to achieve proper time management?

If you know you only have an hour a day to work, would it help keep you focused?

Always focus on your initial reason for doing work in the first place.

After all that reason is still there until you reach your goal.

Create a schedule for your day to keep you from getting distracted.

Distractions are everywhere.

It pops up on your phone.

It pops up from people wanting to chat at work.

It pops up in the form of personal problems.

Whatever it may be, distractions are abound.

The only cure is clear concentration.

To have clear concentration it must be something you are excited about.

To have clear knowledge that this action will lead you to something exciting.

If you find the work boring, It will be difficult for you to concentrate too long.

Sometimes it takes reassessing your life and admitting your work is boring for you to consider a change in direction.

Your goal will have more than one path.

Some paths boring, some paths dangerous, some paths redundant, and some paths magical.

You may not know better until you try.

After all the journey is everything.

If reaching your goal takes decades of work that makes you miserable, is it really worth it?

The changes to your personality may be irreversible.

Always keep the goal in mind whilst searching for an enjoyable path to attain it.

After all, if you are easily distracted from your goal, then do you really want it?

Ask yourself the hard questions.

Is this something you really want? Or is this something society wants for you?

Many people who appear successful to society are secretly miserable.

Make sure you are aware of every little detail of your life.

Sit down and really decide what will make you happy at the end of your life.

What work will you be really happy to do?

What are the causes and people you would be happy to serve?

How much money you want?

What kind of relationships you want?

If you can build a clear vision of this life for you, distractions will become irrelevant.

Irrelevant because nothing will be able to distract you from your perfect vision.

Is what you are doing right now moving you towards that life?

If not stop and start doing the things what will.

It really is that simple.

Anyone who is distracted for too long from the task in hand has no business doing that task. They should instead be doing something that makes them happy.

We can't be happy all the time otherwise we wouldn't be able to recognize it.

But distraction is a clear indicator you may not be on the right path for you.

Clearly define your path and distraction will be powerless.

Chapter 26:

Keep Moving When Things Get Hard

Keep to your goals by putting problems into perspective.

In times of difficulty, most give up.

Don't be like those people.

Difficulties are there to challenge us.

Difficulties are there to help us think outside the box.

Seek to change as you seek success.

Things never really stay the same.

Paths are never that straight.

You always come to a fork in the road.

Think of this new life and realize that thoughts will change how you act.

To have of a better life you must first consider losing this one you have now.

To achieve an extreme desired change, you lose everything in the process.

It can be a tough pill to swallow.

It can be hard to see the silver lining.

But if you can keep moving towards what you have in mind,

sooner or later the new life will start to take shape.

First you must be unwavering in your faith.

It will get hard before it gets easy.

You must endure the winter to see the spring and summer.

You must weather the storm to see the sunshine.

Hard times come to all those who seek success.

Your courage will be tested.

Your endurance and persistence will be tested.

No one is exempt from this price.

You will find that nearly all your life's problems come from fear, loss, and pain,

but they are not as powerful as they appear.

They are no match for you if you believe that.

They are illusions.

Illusions because they are only real in our minds if we allow them to fester.

Most of your perceived problems never actually happened.

Most of your fears were phantoms of the mind.

Be prepared to lose it all if you desire a new life.

You must push through the pain to receive the gain.

In times of pain and struggle, you will grow.

In times of uncertainty, your bravery will shine through.

If you persist, you will make it through any problem.

You will become successful.

You must defeat the 3 phantoms to reach the promised land of health, happiness, and wealth.

Self-mastery is not a battle with yourself.

Self-mastery is letting your inner self take control.

The more you listen to your gut feeling the better your choices.

Your inner voice knows far more than your brain can tell you.

Problems arise because you have not taken action.

Force that change upon yourself.

You are like a shark.

You will die if you stop moving forward.

You will die if you accept defeat.

You must move forward like a shark.

No matter what,

Just keep swimming.

No matter what,

Get to your desired location

Get tough with yourself.

The outcome hangs in the balance.

Trust your inner compass to guide you.

Help who you can along the way.

Your thoughts will become reality good or bad.

Remain focus on the good despite the bad.

Lasting success is waiting for you.

YOU WILL MAKE IT as long as YOU DON'T QUIT!

Persistence is key.

Persist in getting what you want.

Persist in fighting for the job you desire.

Never give up even if you get rejected 100 times over.

Persistence always pays off.

You will be given your chance to shine if you keep at it.

Life will throw you curveballs.

As long as you are moving forward, you can still change direction.

Keep the dream in mind as you navigate through this uncharted territory.

No matter what,

Belief in yourself and your vision.

Keep trying to find the best people for your organization and look after them like family.

One action can change your whole situation.

One action can change your entire life.

You will overcome the obstacles if you keep going and keep believing.

Nothing is more powerful than a made-up mind.

Chapter 27:

Live Life To The Fullest

Have you ever felt like others don't understand your pain when they seem to be living a happy life? You're not alone in feeling this way, but the truth is that happiness takes work, and learning how to live life to the fullest takes dedication and practice.

People who smile in public have been through every bit as much as people who cry, frown, and scream. They just simply found the courage and strength to smile through it and enjoy life in the best way possible.

Life is short, and we only live once. Learning to live life to the fullest is an important step in making the most of every day.

Whether it's taking care of your children, working hard on your career, writing a new blog post each day, or baking up fabulous creations, you get to decide how you enjoy spending your time. Your parents, friends, community, and society in general all have their opinions, but at the end of the day, you're the only person who will be around for every moment of your life.

Do what makes you happy, and everything else will fall into place. This may not mean finding your perfect job if you're limited by education, location, or job openings. However, you can still do what you love by engaging in hobbies, volunteer work, or mentoring.

Sometimes there's danger involved in life, but every reward carries risk with it. If you never take risks, you'll never get anywhere in life, and you certainly won't learn how to live life to the fullest.

Staying in your comfort zone is the fastest way to become discontent Without stepping outside what you're already comfortable with, you will cease to learn and stagnate in both your personal and professional life. While it may feel uncomfortable, taking a risk can be as simple as saying yes next time your friends want to go out instead of staying at home alone. It can mean going out on a blind date, buying plane tickets to a new city, or dragging out those paints that have been stuffed away for years.

When people look back on their lives, they regret the chances they didn't take more than the ones they did, so find something new to try today and set goals beyond what you currently believe possible.

You'll hear people say, "I had that idea," every time you see someone create something great. Everyone had the idea for Facebook first. The reason Mark Zuckerberg got rich off of it is because he went out and did it while everyone else was talking about it. Learning to live life to the fullest is a big step in discovering a path that will lead you to your greatest sense of happiness and accomplishment. We all need moments to rest and relish in a sense of contentment but staying in one place too long will leave you feeling a lack in life. Discover what makes your life feel meaningful and go after it.

Chapter 28:

Removing The Things In Your Day That Don't Serve A Purpose for You

Today I went to a yoga class and felt that something was not quite right. I did not enjoy it as much as I used to. As I was acting out the poses that the teacher was instructing to us, I found myself wondering what the heck I was doing on my yoga mat. Something I used to look forward everyday suddenly became a chore to me, and I didn't understand why.

I had been forcing myself for the past month thinking that I needed the class to stretch and to feel more flexible. But the more i attended, the unhappier I was. And it was only after I decided to completely remove yoga from my itinerary did, I feel my day was actually more enjoyable.

Many times, we plan things in our day just for the sake of it. We plan things because we think we have to, even if it didn't bring much joy into our lives.

I would like you to think of some of the things in your week, what are those that don't bring joy to you? Could you replace them with something that you might find a little more enjoyable instead?

I believe that many of us try to pack so much into our schedule thinking that the busier we are, the more meaningful our lives are, the more we are getting out of it. While it might be true to a certain extent, over doing and over subscribing can actually be counter-productive for us. All of us need rest and relaxation to recharge and tackle the next day. If we are packing our schedule of things we hate, we will never truly be at peace in life. It is okay to stop the things that stop bringing you joy, and maybe coming back to it at a later time.

I found myself loving to spend time stretching by myself while listening to music rather than doing it in a yoga class. And as soon as I replaced this block of time with something that I enjoyed, it made my day that much better, even if it was just a little.

Start taking a hard look at everything we are putting our time, energy, and commitment to, what are the areas that we should trim that don't serve us anymore, and how can we either replace them with something better or just freeing up time to rest and sleep instead until we figure it out.

You may find yourself just a little bit happier.

Chapter 29:

The Keys To Happiness

If I ask you "what is happiness?", then what would your answer be? It's probably difficult to come up with a simple answer. Yet, here you are, looking for a key to happiness and how to lead a fulfilling life.

The truth is that a universal key to happiness is a myth.

That doesn't mean that you should stop looking for yours right now, it only means that you need to be careful when reading articles about "a key to happiness". The universal key to happiness is non-existent because happiness is one of the most difficult things in life to define.

Now, let's go back to that difficult question: "what is happiness?"

Have you thought about it already? Let me give you an example of how hard it is to define happiness.

Right now, I'm drinking a cup of coffee while writing the outline of this article about how to define happiness. Am I happy right now? Yes, I'm feeling pretty happy:

- I've got nothing to worry about.
- All my basic needs are met.
- The weather is nice.

- I'm going outside in a couple of minutes to go for a walk.

These things are all making me feel pretty happy right now.

By that logic, let's define my happiness as follows:

"Happiness is when I'm in a worry-free state, the weather is nice, everybody I know is alright and I can enjoy a hot cup of coffee."

Voila. There it is. My definition of happiness.

The keys to my happiness are obvious now, and I know enough in order to lead the happiest life I can. I just need to focus on the things I listed above.

Wait a second... If it were this simple, then why have I ever been unhappy?

You might have guessed it already, but I made a very simple error. I assumed that what makes me happy today will make me happy for the rest of my life. And that's just wrong.

Happiness is something that not only changes from person to person, but it's also constantly evolving from day to day.

Your definition of happiness changes over time. This is why happiness is such a difficult concept, and why there's not a single "key to happiness".

Whoever tells you otherwise is likely not aware that people change, and that people don't always share the same values, goals, and purposes.

For a minute, I want you to do consider your own happiness. I want you to think back of last week and consider what things you did that had a positive effect on your happiness.

What things had a significant influence on your mood? What comes to your mind?

Was it spending time with your friends? Was it a great movie you watched? Did you attend an exciting sports event? Or did you enjoy sipping hot coffee on a sunny Wednesday morning? It could obviously be just about anything!

The most important thing to remember when trying to define your keys to a happy and fulfilling life is simple:

There is no universal key that leads to your happiness. That's because your happiness is unique in each and every single way

Chapter 30:

The Power of Contentment

Today we're going to talk about why contentment is possibly a much more attainable and sustainable alternative than trying to achieve happiness.

As we have briefly gone through in the previous video, happiness is a state of mind that is fleeting and never truly lasts for too very long before the opposing forces of sadness and feelings of boredom start creeping in.

Happiness is a limited resource that needs energy and time to build, and we can never really be truly happy all the time. But what about the notion of contentment?

Contentment is a state of feeling that you are satisfied with the current situation, and it need not go beyond that. When we say we are contented with our circumstances, with our jobs, with our friends, family, and relationships, we are telling ourselves that we have enough, and that we can and should be grateful for the things we have instead of feeling lacking in the things we don't.

Many a times when i ask myself if i am happy about something, be it a situation that I had found myself in, or the life that I am living, majority of the time the answer is a resounding no. And it is not because I am unhappy per se, but if i were to ask myself honestly, I can't bring myself to say that yes absolutely that all is great and that I am 100$% truly happy with everything. I have to say that this is my own personal experience, and it may not be an accurate representation of how you see life.

However, if I were to reframe and ask myself this question of "Am I Contented with my life?" I can with absolute confidence say yes I am. I may not have everything in the world, but i can most definitely say I am contented with my job, my friends, my family, my career, my relationships, and my health and body. That I do not need to keep chasing perfection in order to be contented with myself.

You will find that as you ask yourself more and more if you are contented, and if the answer is mostly a yes, you will gradually feel a shift towards a feeling that actually life is pretty good. And that your situation is actually very favourable. Yes, you may not be happy all the time, but then again who is? As long as you are contented 90% of the time, you have already won the game of life. And when you pair contentment with a feeling of gratefulness of the things you have, you will inevitably feel a sense of happiness without having to ask yourself that question or be trying to chase it down on a daily basis.

Many a times when I looked at my current situation to see if I was on the right track, I look around me and I feel that whilst there may be areas that I am lacking and certainly needs improvement, in the grand scheme of things, I am pretty well off and i am contented.

So, I challenge all of you today to look at your life in a different perspective. Start asking yourself the right question of "are you contented", and if by any chance you are not majority of the time, look at what you can do to change things up so that you do feel that life is indeed great and worth living.

CPSIA information can be obtained
at www.ICGtesting.com
Printed in the USA
BVHW091145200922
647493BV00009B/1092